SONGS and STORIES
of the
NORTH AMERICAN INDIANS

SONGS and STORIES
of the
NORTH AMERICAN INDIANS

With Rhythm Indications for Drum Accompaniment

Adapted by PAUL GLASS
Department of Music, Brooklyn College
of the City University of New York

Line drawings by H. B. VESTAL

GROSSET & DUNLAP · Publishers · NEW YORK

ACKNOWLEDGMENT

The songs and stories in this book are based upon studies in the
Bulletins of the Bureau of American Ethnology. Other sources are:
George Catlin, *The North American Indians;* Henry Rowe School-
craft, *Information Respecting the Indian Tribes of North America;*
Frances Densmore, *The American Indians and their Music;* and
the *Annual Reports of the Bureau of American Ethnology.*

fOReWORO

This book presents the stories and songs of five tribes of the North American Indians, the Yuma, Mandan, Teton Sioux, Pawnee and Papago. They are the true authors of these stories and composers of these songs, from which we can learn much about the Indians as people.

The Indians were really the first ones to discover America. Many years before the time of Christopher Columbus, bands of hunters traveled across the Bering Strait connecting Asia and Alaska and wandered to different parts of North America. When Columbus arrived in 1492, he mistakenly called the natives Indians because he thought he had landed in India. After many years, the Indians became good farmers, good hunters of the buffalo, and brave warriors. Their villages were in many parts of the country.

Singing and storytelling gave the Indians pleasure. These diversions also brought the tribe together by providing a feeling of "belonging" and pride. There were four different categories of songs or stories. First, the sacred or religious kind, such as "Wakan'tanka Hears Me," sung by the Teton Sioux at the Sun Dance ceremony. When the Papago Indians prayed for rain, they sang, "I Bring the Rain" and "The Song of the Watchers." A second category included stories and songs originating from dreams, such as "The Horsemen in the Cloud," "The Sacred Stones," and "The Bear is Pointing at the Sun." The third type came from old legends which became a faith with the tribe. "The Traveling Deer" was such a legend, and Yuma Indians believed that the deer had the power to make other animals sing. The fourth category had stories and songs of games and of fun. Such songs were "We Must Run," "I Will Toss Up the Sticks," and the moccasin and "hand game guessing" songs. The Mandan Indians were always fond of joking — the story of the Elk Woman and the song, "The Kettle is Burning," are examples of their humor.

The drum was often an accompaniment to the singing of these songs. An *X* on the line above each melody in this book designates a drum beat.

Lacking a drum, you may use a stick or a pencil and tap it on a box. Three songs do not have drum beats indicated — and so you will have a chance to make up your own.

Bear in mind that these are old songs. When they were originated, the Indians had their own primitive instruments, such as drums, rattles, whistles and flutes. Their melodies, therefore, are different from the songs of today. I have made some changes in the melodies so that the words will fit well with the song, yet retain the original mood. Try to discover for yourself the feeling and mood of each song as part of the story.

Besides the stories and songs, a short history of each tribe is included. I hope this book will give you much pleasure and help you to know more about the American Indians. As President John F. Kennedy once said, ". . . their history is our history and should be part of our remembered heritage."

Paul Glass

contents

(Entries in italics refer to songs.)

the yuma indians

On the eastern bank of the Colorado River (near today's city of Yuma, Arizona) is a beautiful valley where the Yuma Indians made their home. The houses were built of cottonwood poles, the roofs thatched with straw and clay. Beans, corn, pumpkins, melons and nuts were grown in the fields, and a young man was expected to raise enough produce to last almost a year. Yuma tribesmen sometimes held what was called a "burning hunt." A thick brush was set afire while the men waited with bows and arrows to aim at whatever animal ran from it. For this hunt they wore sandals that had soles of heavy hide.

Many travelers and missionaries who visited the Yuma described them as tall, strong and friendly. Older men wore their hair long, often down to the waist. Others braided it in a high twist on top of the head and covered it with a handkerchief. Women cut their hair a bit below the shoulders and wore it loose. When a girl was fifteen years old, straight lines were tattooed on her chin, which assured that she would go "straight to the spirit land" when she died. Without the tattoo, "her spirit would wander." Both men and women wore gay cotton mantles of bright red and blue colors.

Legends

The Yuma have many legends about the beginning of their tribe. The oldest story relates that all tribes were sent out from a high mountain where there was a big square with little foot marks in the rock. To the Yuma were given arrowwood for building houses, as well as a place where they could fish and hunt wild deer.

Another legend asserts that they came from a large body of water, and at every place the Yuma camped they made fires, traces of which can still be seen today. Water was called "mother" and the sun "father." The sun called the earth up from below the water. They met and kissed, and then the sun pulled back to the sky, but the earth stayed where it was. Where the earth and the sky came apart, the highest points of the sunken earth became mountains of hard rock. *Yuma* is said to mean "Sons of the River."

Life in the Tribe

Yuma parents began to teach their children at a very early age. A charm in the shape of a chain was made from the four longest hairs in a horse's tail and hung around the child's neck; it was believed that this would make the child grow quickly and give him strength. At the age of seven, a child was expected to help with the daily duties of the tribe. A girl had to learn to prepare food and grind grain on stone.

10

Medicine men held a round white stone (like a marble) in their mouth when treating the sick, which was believed to bring success in their treatment.

Picture writing was used to tell a story and keep records. Straight and curved lines painted on rocks recorded the ages of the men. Other signs would tell about the coming of a big feast, or about preparation for a hunt.

Today about a thousand Yuma Indians live and work on the eastern side of the Colorado River, directly across from Fort Yuma, where the U. S. Bureau of Indian Affairs helps direct their activities.

Songs and Musical Instruments

The only drum used by the Yuma was a basket which was struck with willow sticks or the palm of the hand. Flutes were made from the bamboo plant. The Yuma's song was generally the kind that told a story about animals like the deer, the frog, the coyote and the birds. Singing such stories, along with dancing and drumming, provided great pleasure.

The Traveling Deer

The story of Akwa'k the deer was told in song and dance, and had a special meaning for the Yuma Indians, who believed that the deer had some mysterious power to make other animals sing.

It was told during the summer at the time of a full moon. Men painted their skin and wore an animal's tail or the head of a deer. Sometimes a man wore the hide of a wildcat on his head, its paws hanging down on each side of his face. The animal's tail hung on the dancer's belt at the back. When the male dancer stamped his right foot, he dipped his right hand below his knee; at the same time, he put his left hand and arm behind him. He reversed these movements when he stamped his left foot. Then the men and women joined in a circle, holding hands and moving clockwise with a swaying motion from left to right.

The singers were seated on three separate overturned baskets, four singers at each basket. A leading singer of each group struck the basket with two willow sticks, while the others struck it with the palm of their right hand.

It took a full night to tell the story. Every part of the night had a special song which described the deer's journey and the animals he met.

Let us follow the deer on his journey and sing about his adventures.

the deer begins his travels

Walking Time ♩ = **92**

The deer is trav-el-ing, The deer is trav-el-ing, Down the moun-tain, Down the moun-tain, From the head___ wa-ters of the Col-o-rad-o Riv-er, Trav-el-ing all a-lone,

The deer continued moving in a southwesterly direction, passing through Indio, California, and eventually reached the mountains. At the summit of one he enjoyed the breezes bringing the scent of the western ocean. Then, after resting for a while, he walked down the cliffs and wandered along the beach, where before long he heard splashing sounds. A large water bug was chasing a sunfish. The bug made large ripples and shadows in the water. As the deer looked at the shadows, he said, "The water bug brings the darkness and it will soon be night." Slowly and quietly he came closer to the bobbing water bug and stared at him. Then the deer requested the water bug to sing for him, so the bug told why he bobs about.

13

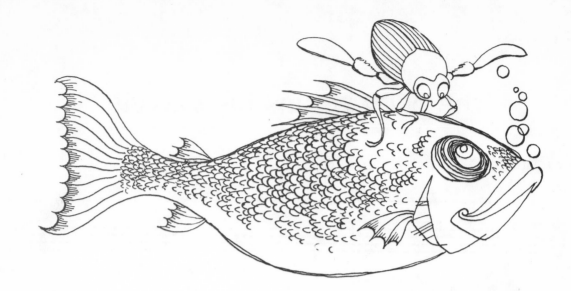

the WATER BUG stands upon a fish

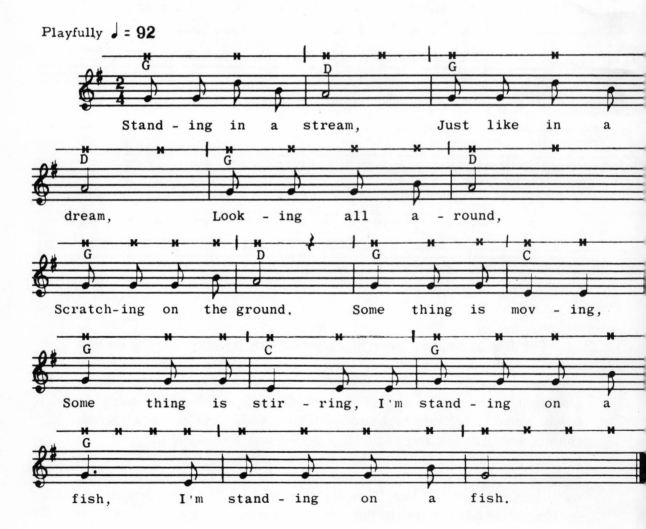

Playfully ♩ = 92

Stand - ing in a stream, Just like in a dream, Look - ing all a - round, Scratch-ing on the ground, Some thing is mov - ing, Some thing is stir - ring, I'm stand - ing on a fish, I'm stand - ing on a fish.

14

Soon the evening shadows became darker. The deer knew that the water bug brought the shadows and he called it "darkness." As he rested, he sang this song:

from daylight to darkness

Slowly and quietly ♩ = 72

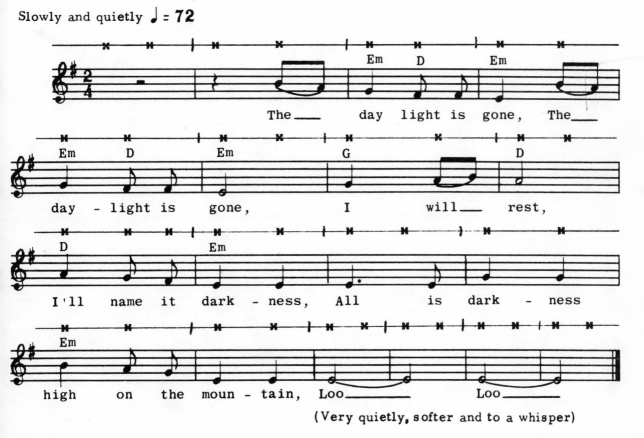

The___ day light is gone, The___ day - light is gone, I will___ rest, I'll name it dark - ness, All is dark - ness high on the moun - tain, Loo_____ Loo_____

(Very quietly, softer and to a whisper)

15

When the deer had been in the darkness a long time, he met a spider. "How can I travel in the darkness?" he asked the spider. The spider replied, "I will build you a road." All through the night the spider worked. The deer asked the spider to sing, and the song helped the spider build the road in faster time. The road was a long thread of spider web which guided the deer out of the darkness. When he reached the daylight, he shook himself.

the spider makes a road

The deer decided to travel eastward, on the way back to where he had started his journey. He reached the Colorado River and called it "Red River." (At some parts of the river, the red earth and clay is washed down from the shore, which makes the water reddish.) After crossing the mountains, he came to Phoenix, where the sun shines brightly in the morning. He saw a flock of blackbirds and asked them to sing for him. And the blackbirds sang:

SONG OF THE BLACKBIRDS

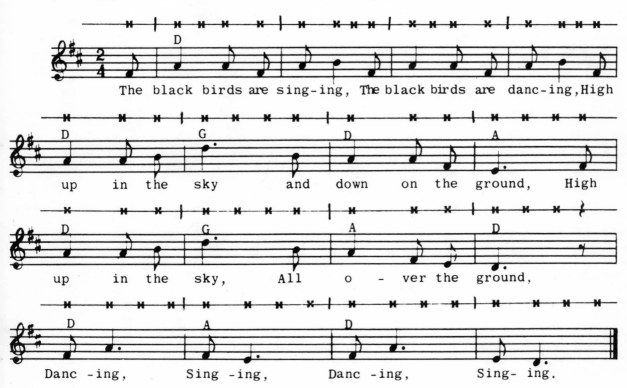

Lively ♩ = 112

The black birds are sing-ing, The black birds are danc-ing, High
up in the sky and down on the ground, High
up in the sky, All o - ver the ground,
Danc -ing, Sing -ing, Danc -ing, Sing- ing.

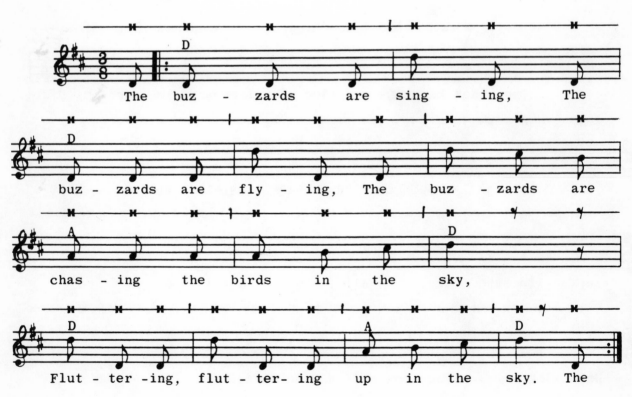

As the blackbirds were singing, some large buzzards came flying to the scene.

"Join us and sing one of your songs," cried the deer.

At first the buzzards chased the other birds, but they soon returned and sang this song:

SONG OF THE BUZZARDS

Gay and Happy ♩ = 118

The buz - zards are sing - ing, The buz - zards are fly - ing, The buz - zards are chas - ing the birds in the sky, Flut - ter -ing, flut - ter-ing up in the sky. The

18

The deer continued eastward over the Rocky Mountains, going through a thick forest of giant oaks and redwoods. Not far away, a beautiful redbird was flitting about, chirping cheerfully. The redbird kept coming closer.

"Your colors are so bright — they are like the trees," said the deer.

"This is my home and I love to fly in it," answered the redbird.

"Sing me a song about the forest," requested the deer.

The redbird told the deer that she had a dream about the clouds and the winds, and how she flew about in the air with her fledglings. She made up a song about her dream and sang:

the REDBIRD SINGS

Movingly ♩ = 104

This is my air, The won - der - ful air,

These are my clouds, On winds___ they glide,

These are my trees that sway in the breeze,

Here I will build a nest for my young.

"Your song is very lovely. It tells me that you love your home in the forest. Sing it again," said the deer.

As the redbird sang, a hummingbird came by and perched next to the redbird. She sat quietly and waited for the redbird to finish the song.

Then the hummingbird said, "I am only a simple little hummingbird. I try to enjoy the same things as the redbird. I love the trees, the clouds and the breezes. I want little children to fly in the air."

The redbird and the deer listened. Then the deer said, "Hummingbird, sing a song about the things you want to enjoy and your wish will come true. Sing, hummingbird! Sing!"

And the hummingbird sang:

song of the hummingbird

"You sing so sweetly," said the deer.

"Yes, and her wings move swiftly," remarked the redbird.

Then the hummingbird flew from branch to branch, its wings shining and reflecting all the colors of the rainbow. Both the deer and the redbird watched the hummingbird with wonder and joy.

Soon evening shadows entered the forest, and an owl joined the company. The deer asked the owl to sing, but the owl only hooted.

Then the deer asked again, "Sing to us about what you know best." The owl sang about the evening star and the shadows.

the owl sings

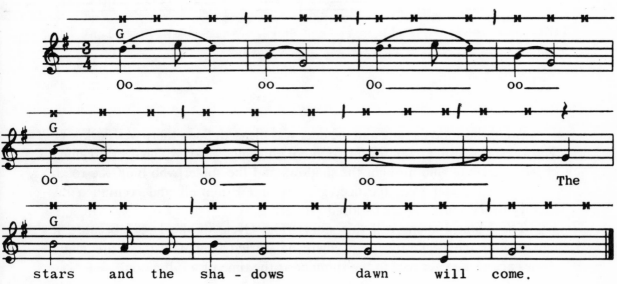

Slowly ♩ = **80**

Oo_____ oo_____ Oo_____ oo_____

Oo____ oo_____ oo_____ The

stars and the sha - dows dawn will come.

Swiftly and with a cheerful chirp, the nighthawk arrived, hopping from tree branch to tree branch, and assured the birds and the deer not to fear the evening shadows.

"The daylight will soon be here and all will be bright and gay," he declared.

"Sing a song about the daylight," said the deer.

The nighthawk kept moving from one branch to another. Then he rested on a branch near the owl and sang about the daylight that would soon come.

song of the nighthawk

Moderate ♩ = 100

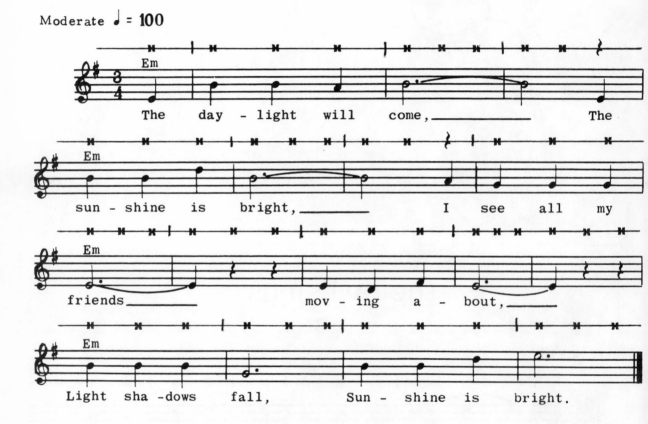

The day - light will come, _____ The sun - shine is bright, _____ I see all my friends _____ mov - ing a - bout, _____ Light sha -dows fall, Sun - shine is bright.

All of the animals sang and the deer was pleased. Soon there was darkness. The forest was still, except for the sound of chirping crickets. The deer dreamed of the water bug who brought the shadows and the spider who built the road.

When the sun rose, the deer got up, shook himself and continued his journey to the source of the Colorado River.

The Yuma Indians call this story "The Cycle of the Deer" because it tells of how the deer returns to where he started. But now there are many stories about the deer told in the summer at the time of a full moon.

22

the mandan indians

The American artist, George Catlin, visited the Mandan Indians in 1832, at which time he wrote, "They are very interesting and pleasant people. They are handsome, straight and elegant in their forms . . . not tall, but quick and graceful; easy and polite in manners, neat in their persons and beautifully clad. They are not warlike people and seldom fight with other tribes."

George Catlin painted many pictures of this tribe. Once, as they looked on, he painted a picture of their chieftain, *Mah-to-toh-pa* (the name means "Four Bears"), whose decorated costume told the history of the tribe.

The early homes of the Mandan were on the western side of the Missouri River in North Dakota. In 1845 the tribe moved up the river and built villages near the trading post of Fort Berthold. On March 3, 1891, the United States Congress fixed the land boundaries for the Fort Berthold Reservation. (There were about 1,600 Mandan Indians living in 1850; at the present time, about four hundred live on the reservation.)

Mandan homes were round earth-covered lodges, overlooking the river. The housetops were used for many purposes — to store sleds, boats, pottery and buffalo skins. In the evening a family would gather there to sing and play games. It was a pleasant aspect of village life.

Legends

The story about the beginnings of the tribe was told to the explorers Lewis and Clark when they visited the Mandan in the winter of 1804.

Long ago, it was said, the entire Mandan tribe lived beneath the earth near a lake. The roots of a grapevine grew down to their home and daylight was seen. Through the help of several animals, some people climbed up the grapevine to explore.

They were delighted with the sight of the earth which they found abundant with buffalo and rich with every kind of fruit. More men, women and children decided to leave the underground home. But when about half of the tribe had reached the surface, the weight of a very fat woman broke the vine, and part of the tribe remained below.

Good Fur Robe was the leader of the Mandans. He taught them how to live in their new surroundings. The Mandan believed that their name came from the Indian word *minatarees,* which means "people of the willow."

Some Mandan Indians on the Fort Berthold Reservation today still speak of Good Fur Robe as a leader who did wonderful things for the tribe.

Musical Instruments

The Mandan made drums, rattles, whistles and flutes. The drums, about eighteen inches wide, were covered with deerskin. Some were made of hide stretched over a turtle's shell. The rattle was a shell filled with small stones and attached to a colored stick. Whistles were made from the wing bone of birds. Some whistles were made from the quills of a large bird and measured between four and five inches in length. The flute was made from box wood — it was about ten inches long and had seven holes, evenly spaced. This instrument could sound many notes so that a musician could play melodies.

Singing was an enjoyable part of Mandan village life. It was always a part of the ceremony and the storytelling hour.

The Story of the Flute

"Who is ruining my garden?" cried Old Granny. All the cornstalks, sun-flowers and vegetables were crushed. As she looked around, Granny observed some footprints and arrows. She decided to set a trap to catch the guilty one.

Back in her house she made a kick-ball, such as is used by Indian boys in their games. She also made a bow and some arrows. The kick-ball was placed in the garden and the bow and the arrows were placed near a tree. Now she would wait and watch.

Very soon she saw a little boy shooting the arrows into the kick-ball. Old Granny rushed out of the house and grabbed him.

"Why are you doing this?" she asked.

"My dead mother is buried around here, someplace," cried the little boy.

"Let us go and see," said Old Granny.

The child was very young and could not tell how it all happened. When Old Granny found the mother's grave, she decided to take the little boy into her house and be a mother to him.

The little boy liked Old Granny's place. She taught him how to cook

25

food, how to fish, and how to hunt. She also taught him how to take care of himself away from home.

One day the little boy started out by himself and came to a place where two hunters were butchering a buffalo. One of the hunters, a rough fellow, shouted at him, "Take this home to your Granny and she will cook it for you. We want Granny to take care of us, too."

The frightened boy ran away and climbed up a tree to escape from the hunters.

After two days in the forest, the little boy came home and told Old Granny the whole story. "So the hunters frightened you, did they?" said Old Granny. "Well, we will teach them a lesson!"

She went into the field and cut a large sunflower stalk, from which she made a flute with seven holes. Each hole was for one of the seven months of the winter season. Old Granny taught the little boy to play a melody on her flute which she said would cause snow to fall. Old Granny had an idea for punishing the hunters.

Granny clothed the boy from head to foot in smoked buffalo hide and directed him to travel in four circles, each smaller than the one before, playing the flute all the while. The first circle was to be at the foot of the clouds, the horizon, and the last (fourth) circle would bring him near the hunters. Old Granny said, "When you are near the hunters, they will know it. Just keep playing the flute."

The boy started out and traveled in a circle at the foot of the clouds, playing on the flute, and soon the snow began to fall.

The hunters said, "Something is wrong." They built a lodge for shelter until the snow would stop falling. But the snow continued to fall, covering the lodge until only its peak was above the snow.

One of the hunters said, "Something is causing this." And the other said, "It must be so."

The boy kept circling closer, playing on his flute, and the snow kept falling. The hunters had no food to eat and only melted snow to drink.

When the boy came into sight, he said, "Now it is my turn to make you do something for me."

After talking it over, the hunters agreed that the boy would be called Father and the hunters would be his sons. They promised to bring him gifts of food and clothing. The boy stopped his playing on the flute and the snow stopped falling. The boy then made all the snow disappear. And since he was now called Father, he had to make his sons comfortable, so he got them some game and firewood.

When the boy returned home, Old Granny said, "What have you done?"

The little boy told her, and old Granny was pleased. "That is good. You gave them some of their own treatment," she said.

The two hunters came to Old Granny's lodge and told her that they would soon return with many gifts of food and clothing. The little boy who was now called Father waved good-by to the hunters and called out to them, "Good hunting — and come back soon!"

song of the flute

To Be Sung On The Sound Of LOO

Walking Style ♩ = 72

The Coyote and the Skunk

A coyote and a skunk were both hungry. They hunted and sniffed around the stumps of old trees and rocks for many hours, but they could not find enough food.

The coyote at last thought of a plan. "Let us make up a play and go over to the prairie-dog village to get some food," he said.

The coyote went to the lake and got some hollow reeds. He cut them into sections about a foot long and tied several to each ear of the skunk and also to the tail. He told the skunk to dance and when the skunk did so, the hollow reeds rattled. The coyote decided that the skunk should dance and sing and he would be the drummer. He cut two drumsticks from a long thick branch, and then together they went to the prairie-dog village.

As the two approached the village, the prairie dogs cried out, "Come and see the wonderful thing that has come to our village!" The skunk sang and danced, and the coyote drummed.

Slowly, the skunk and the coyote moved away from the village. The prairie dogs did not really notice this because they were fascinated by the singing, dancing and drumming, so they followed the skunk and the coyote.

While the skunk sang and danced, the coyote, unseen by the prairie dogs, ran back to the village. He found lots of food, which he gulped down, but he left some for his partner, the skunk. Then the coyote ran back to the place where the skunk was singing. He drummed, he sang, he rolled over, he tossed the drumsticks into the air, and he hopped on his hind legs.

As the prairie dogs watched, entranced, the skunk stole away to the village for his share of the food.

The skunk came back soon to join his partner, the drumming coyote. They both continued singing and drumming for a while longer.

When the entertainment was finished, the prairie dogs began growling and barking — they wanted more singing and dancing. But the coyote and the skunk snarled back. Then the prairie dogs barked at them and chased them away. When they returned to their village, the prairie dogs discovered that all of their food was gone.

So the tricky coyote fooled the prairie dogs. His ruse of singing, dancing and drumming had worked, and they were no longer hungry.

The Skunk Society

Mandan Indian girls from eight to thirteen years of age belong to the Skunk Society. When a hunting party returns to the tribe, the girls sing for the hunters in the evening. For this the hunters reward the girls with gifts.

The girls wear an upright eagle feather at the back of the head, and on the forehead they place a triangle made of white clay tapering toward the nose. This "costume" represents the skunk of the story. Sometimes a young man with a drum leads the singing.

Note to teachers: This story has been made into a recreational exercise. Girls walk in a line singing the song, holding on to the dress of the girl ahead.

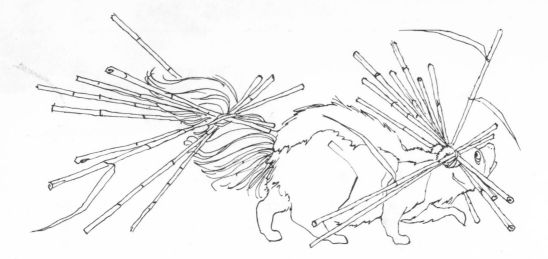

dancing song of the skunk

Cheerfully ♩ = 104

My____ tail it rat-tles, My____ tail it rat-tles,

My____ ears they rat-tle, My____ ears they rat-tle,

Ev-'ry end it rat-tles, Ev-'ry end it rat-tles,

My whole bod-y rat-tles, My whole bod-y rat-tles,

My whole face is striped, My whole face is striped,

My whole back is striped, My whole back is striped.

The Elk Woman and the Burning Kettle

This song tells a story about a forgetful Indian woman whose name was Elk Woman. She belonged to a song-and-dance group called the Elk Society. What happened in her kitchen can — and does — happen to many women today.

Elk Woman had a large collection of earthen pots. One day she was cooking a corn mush in one of her many pots. Some Mandan Indian women call this corn mush a "stir-about" because it must be stirred constantly to prevent it from burning. When Elk Woman saw that her corn mush was running dry, she went out to the well to get some water.

On the way to fetch some water, she met Chief Eagle who was going to a meeting of the Eagle Catching Society. He was wearing a handsome new costume given to him by the hunters of that society. Mandan Indians are known for their beautiful clothes, and Chief Eagle's costume had pictures of the eagle in red and golden colors.

Elk Woman liked the costume and she examined it closely. "Those colors are so bright and gay," she said. Then she touched the buffalo hide and said, "It is so soft and smooth." Then she touched the beaver collar and said with a nod of the head, "So silky and fresh." She looked and touched the eagle feathers of the chief's headdress. She fingered his necklace made of elk teeth. "It is all so nice, so very nice," she said.

Chief Eagle smiled, nodded his head and said many times, "Thank you, thank you, Elk Woman." He was in a hurry to get to his meeting, but he was nevertheless polite and patient. Suddenly he sniffed a few times and cried out, "Elk Woman, Elk Woman, something is burning!"

They both rushed back to the house, only to find that the whole pot of corn mush had burned.

On another day, Elk Woman came to a meeting of the tribe and was greeted with a surprise. As a joke, everybody began singing, "Elk Woman, Elk Woman, your kettle is burning!" Elk Woman had learned her lesson. She joined in the singing with a cheerful smile.

The Elk Society

The elk was a favorite animal with many Indian tribes. A brave hunter would say, "The elk stands for strength and long life. The elk is fast and defends himself well. The elk's tooth will last longer than man. We want long life for our friends. That is why the elk's tooth is given to the parents of a child as a gift. It will bring long life."

the kettle is burning

With Excitement ♩ = 120

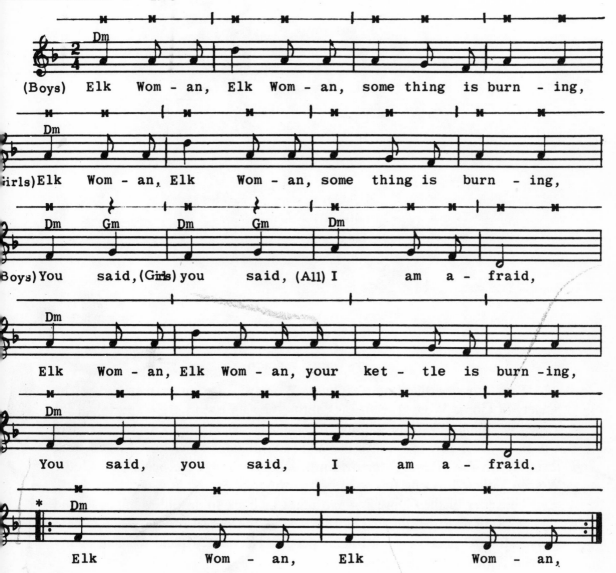

(Boys) Elk Wom - an, Elk Wom - an, some thing is burn - ing,

(Girls) Elk Wom - an, Elk Wom - an, some thing is burn - ing,

(Boys) You said, (Girls) you said, (All) I am a - fraid,

Elk Wom - an, Elk Wom - an, your ket - tle is burn - ing,

You said, you said, I am a - fraid.

*Elk Wom - an, Elk Wom - an,

*Repeat the last two measures as many times as you like, each time playing and singing it more softly, until it is down to a whisper. The tapping rhythms of the stick also become softer.

The Goose Woman

The "Song of the Captive Goose Woman" is about a member of the Society of Goose Women who was captured by an enemy tribe and taken far away. She managed to escape and then started back home. As she traveled, a flock of geese flew low above her and sang a song, which she learned from them. When the Goose Woman returned home safely, the Society of Goose Women gathered to sing this song in her honor.

The story of the Goose Woman takes us back to an old Mandan legend about Good Fur Robe, the first Corn Priest and leader of the tribe who always worked for the greatest good for his people. He wanted them to have plenty of good corn and other vegetables.

Good Fur Robe started the Goose Women Society. He directed the women to tend the corn. He also gave them songs and showed them how to pray for a good harvest. A young man was picked by the chief to teach the songs and sing with the women. If there was an early frost, the women would bring presents to Good Fur Robe, and he would show them how to save the crop. The Goose Women Society held their meetings in the early spring, when they prepared for the planting of the corn.

Mandan Indians believed that the Goose Women had special powers. If a child was sick, its parents would bring presents to the Goose Women so that the sick child would grow strong and sturdy, like young corn. A young man going on a hunt would first ask the Goose Women to bless him and wish him well.

Other ceremonies took place in the early fall, when geese flew away. A woman would say, "I promise, O geese, to give a feast for the Goose Women when you return in the spring." She would then ask her friends to prepare for the feast, and when springtime came, everything was ready. There was singing during the day (many of the songs gave thanks for the food and the good harvest) and dancing in the evening.

The Mandan Indians believed that the goose and the duck were symbols of the corn and beans that grew. And that is why the Society of Goose Women had such an important place in the tribe.

SONG OF THE CAPTIVE GOOSE WOMAN

Not Too Slow ♩ = 84

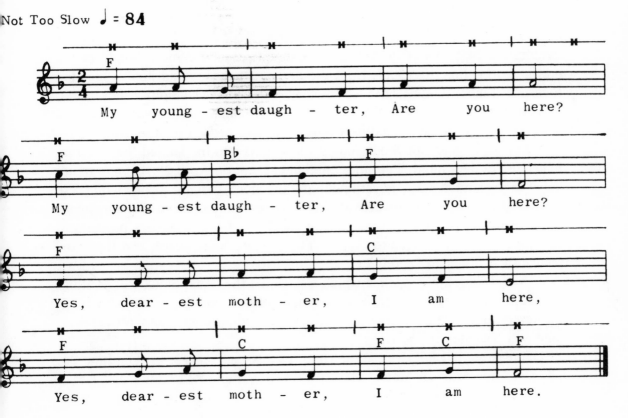

My young - est daugh - ter, Are you here?

My young - est daugh - ter, Are you here?

Yes, dear - est moth - er, I am here,

Yes, dear - est moth - er, I am here.

the teton sioux indians

The Teton Sioux was the largest division of the Dakota Indian tribe. (Seven different bands made up the whole Dakota tribe.) The word Dakota means "allied" — all in one. The Dakota was a league of different bands and they called themselves the "Council of Fires." The word Sioux, given to them by the white man and other Indian tribes who fought them for many years, comes from the Indian word *Nadawessioux,* which means "enemies." There were more than ten thousand Sioux living in the northern plains around Minnesota, North and South Dakota in 1804. In this group were also the Santees, who lived near Devils Lake, North Dakota, and the Yanctons, who lived in South Dakota.

In olden times, the Sioux would gather during the summer when everything looked beautiful. The purpose of the happy gathering was to hear about the deeds of other bands, to tell stories about brave warriors and brave hunters, and to hear the songs of the brother Indian bands. Another reason for the gathering was to hear the new laws made by the head chiefs of the tribe.

The Sioux were good farmers, good hunters and brave warriors. They raised corn, squash and beans. They also built many towns and villages. Their little "bull boats" sailed down the waterways to trade and bring supplies to other bands of the Dakota tribe. Their costumes were made from deer and buffalo hide, and were decorated with different kinds of feathers. Each feather would tell a story about the deeds of a brave hunter or a brave warrior.

The buffalo was the main source of food for the Plains Indians. Every part of the animal was used. The Indians even made handles for their small hand tools, such as the knife, from different parts of the buffalo. The time for hunting the buffalo was in early fall, when the animal came down from the north. At this time the chiefs from the different bands would hold a meeting to decide if more food was needed for the whole tribe. The Sioux believed that the buffalo was a gift from the Great Spirit, Wakan'tanka. It was considered a sacred animal, to be hunted only when the tribe needed to store food.

For many years the Sioux fought the settlers and the United States Army in defense of their hunting grounds and land. Then, on April 29, 1868, a treaty between the United States government and the Sioux Indians opened with these words: "From this day forward, all war between the parties to this agreement shall forever cease. The government of the United States desires peace, and its honor is hereby pledged to keep it. The Indians desire peace, and they now pledge their honor to keep it."

A reservation was opened which was called the Great Sioux Reservation. By the terms of the treaty, the government placed buildings and schools on the reservation. Under certain conditions, an Indian could get 160 acres of land and become a U. S. citizen.

But peace did not come until 1889, twenty-one years later. On June 25, 1876, a large army of Sioux, headed by Sitting Bull, Red Cloud and Crazy Horse, wiped out five companies of the United States Cavalry led by General

George Armstrong Custer at the Battle of the Little Bighorn, which came to be known as "Custer's Last Stand."

The last time the Sioux tried to free themselves from the reservation was at the Sun Dance of 1881 and the last buffalo hunt in 1882. In 1889, a new reservation was opened in North and South Dakota called "Standing Rock Reservation." The name was later changed to Fort Yates. At this time the Indians gave back to the government nine million acres of land.

Many Sioux Indians, since then, have been attending boarding schools and learning trades. Some have left the reservation and have taken their place among other communities.

The Sun Dance

The Sun Dance was the most important ceremony of the Teton Sioux Indians, at which time the tribe offered to the Great Spirit Wakan'tanka the strongest and the best that was in them. It was an honor to be chosen for a leading part in the Sun Dance, for many brave hunters and warriors were picked for such a part. Some of them were: Red Bird, Buffalo Boy, Lone Man, Charging Thunder, and Chased-by-Bears.

The ceremony took place in midsummer, at the time of a full moon. The trees were in full bloom and the June berries were ripe. Many Indians traveled a long distance and brought their tents with them. A month before the Sun Dance, the medicine men prayed for good weather, singing, burning sweet grass and offering their pipes to the sky.

The Sun Dance began within a great circle of tents. A buffalo skull was placed in the center, facing west. Then a chief, standing near the skull, spoke this prayer: "Wakan'tanka, hear me. This day I am to tell your word. I shall speak without sin. The tribe shall live. I am humble. From above, watch me. You are always the truth. Listen to me. I shall be at peace. May our voices be heard."

Seated in the center of the circle, the chiefs listened. Silently, the pipe was passed from one to another, each man puffing it for a moment. The closest attention was given to the prayer.

Then twenty men were picked to place four sacred twenty-five-foot poles in the center of the circle. As they marched in, the medicine men said, "Now we must sing and make a wish." Everybody sang and wished for a good harvest. Next came the dancers, each painted in a favorite color. Blue was for the clear sky, red was for the sunset, and yellow for the lightning. They sang and danced for the four sacred poles.

Children also took part in the Sun Dance. The girls had their ears pierced and a small piece of metal was placed in the tiny hole. The boys and girls sang and asked Wakan'tanka to send them gifts. They promised to do good deeds.

After many songs and dances, the time came for the giving of gifts. An Indian woman had the honor of making a very beautiful pipe, painted in many colors, which was called the Sun Dance pipe and which she gave to the leader of the Sun Dancers. A rich Sioux chief gave a robe made of buffalo hide to a brave warrior. The Sioux believed all gifts came from Wakan'tanka.

wakan'tanka heaRs me

song of the sacred stones

Chantlike ♩ = 80

The Sacred Stones

Stones have many different shapes and colors. Sometimes, as we look at them, we say, "This part looks like a tree . . . This could be an old man's face . . . I think this one looks like a ship." Some of us may carry a stone with us as a supposed "good luck" piece. The colors and shapes of stones bring many thoughts to our minds. For many years the winds and rains have carved stones into many shapes and colors.

The Teton Sioux believed that certain stones were sacred things and had special powers. The Indian name for them was *tun'kan,* which means "Grandfather." The stones were the native brown sandstone, round or oval-shaped, and slightly flat. A Teton Sioux said, "The holy stone is perfect and is the work of nature. It is like a house where all can dwell safely."

There are many songs about the sacred stones made up from remembered dreams. Brave Buffalo, a Teton Sioux chief, told this story:

"When I was ten years of age, I looked at the land and the rivers, the sky above, and the animals around me. I felt that all this must have been made by some great power. I wanted to understand this power. I looked at the trees, the bushes and the flowers. They all seemed to be staring at me and I wanted to ask them, "Who made you?" I looked at the moss-covered stones; some of them looked like a man, but they could not answer me. Then I had a dream, and one small stone told me that the maker of all things was the Great Spirit, Wakan'tanka, and that I must honor and respect his works in nature. If I am curing a sick person, I might ask the stone for help and all of nature would assist me."

Soon after his dream, Brave Buffalo found, on top of a high mountain, his first sacred stone — a perfect one, round and slightly flat. He painted it in his favorite color, Indian red. Brave Buffalo told his tribe that the stone blessed him when hunting in the forest and also cured many sick Indians of the tribe. He said, "The stones are like the sun and the moon — not buried in the ground, but on top of the hill." Brave Buffalo kept this stone for many years.

Lone Man and the Sacred Stones

Lone Man, one of the older Indians of the tribe, was honored to sing and play the drum in the Sun Dance. He had fought against General Custer in the Battle of the Little Big Horn. Lone Man knew many stories and he told this one to a group of white people who came to visit him.

"When I was young, I went to see a medicine man for advice concerning my future. The medicine man said, 'You must learn all about the earth on which you live. A good hunter must learn the ways of all the animals. He must know all about the forest, the trails and the weather. The earth is large and on it live many animals.'

"The medicine man told me about the herbs and roots in the forest, saying they were made for the benefit of animals and men. Some have different colors and change with the season. The sacred stones will teach you and protect you. Wakan'tanka, the Great Spirit, tells the sacred stones many things. All this the medicine man told me.

"He then gave me a sacred stone which he had worn for many years. I kept it with me wherever I went and was helped by it. He also showed me where I might find one for myself.

"When I went to the forest, I watched the changes of the weather, and the habits of the animals. I looked for trails and listened to many sounds.

"Once I had a dream about the animals in the forest. They came to me and I fed them with herbs and roots. The sacred stones helped me to understand the animals. That is why they came to me.

"One evening I had a dream about a brave warrior being thrown from his horse. He fell to the ground and injured his head. I came to him with my sacred stone. Then I dressed his wounds with the medicine I had made from the herbs. He soon got well and went to find his horse."

When Lone Man finished telling his story, he sang the song about his dream of the animals and how they came to him.

I SING FOR THE ANIMALS

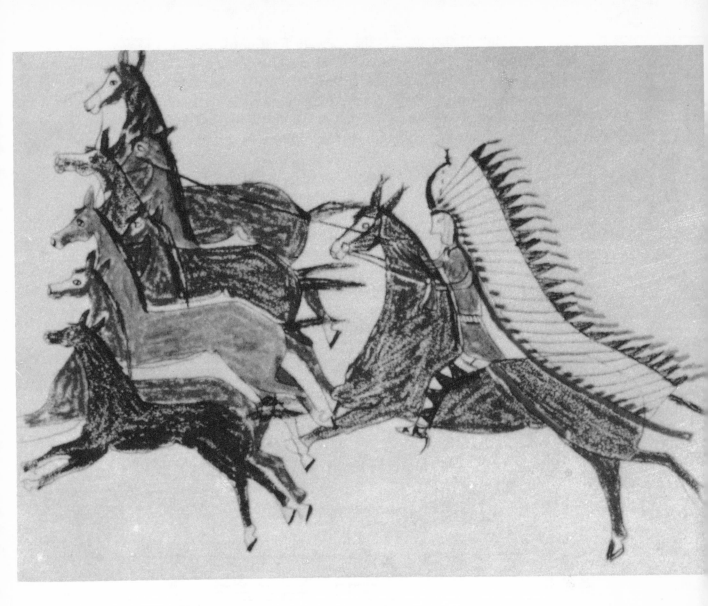

The Horsemen in the Cloud

Dreams about thunder were considered important by the Teton Sioux and had to be reported to the tribe. The dreamer would sing his song about the dream at a ceremony called the *Heyo'ka Ka'ga* and also act it out. Such dreams were called "dreams of the thunderbirds."

Many Indians have told about dreaming of these giant birds flying in the clouds. Some have said that the thunderbirds came to earth as giants who did wonderful things such as digging the ditches where the rivers flow. During this period, rain would fall without any sound of thunder or flash of lightning, but when the giants died of old age, their spirits went back to the clouds and the sounds of thunder were heard again.

Lone Man told this story about his dream of the thunderbirds. (The sacred stones were also a part of this dream.)

"One day when I was on the warpath I sat down to rest. I looked up at the sky and the rolling clouds. I fell asleep, and while I slept I had a dream. My face was toward the west, and I heard thunder. There was a sound of hoofs, and I saw nine riders coming toward me in a cloud, each man on a horse of a different color. Then I heard a sound in the north and saw nine riders coming toward me, each on a white horse. They joined the riders from the west and came toward me.

"Then one of the riders said, 'You will be our leader and attack the enemy.' I found the enemy. I ran at him and my spear killed him. Then I saw him fall and change into a reed standing in the water. All the riders called me a brave warrior. The horsemen in the cloud told me to look down on the earth and learn everything about the land and the water. They told me about the animals that live in the water and also that the water is sent from the sky.

"Before the riders in the sky went away, they gave me a little charm. They said, 'This will guard you and protect you. You will always do good things.' Then the riders taught me this song."

the horsemen in the cloud

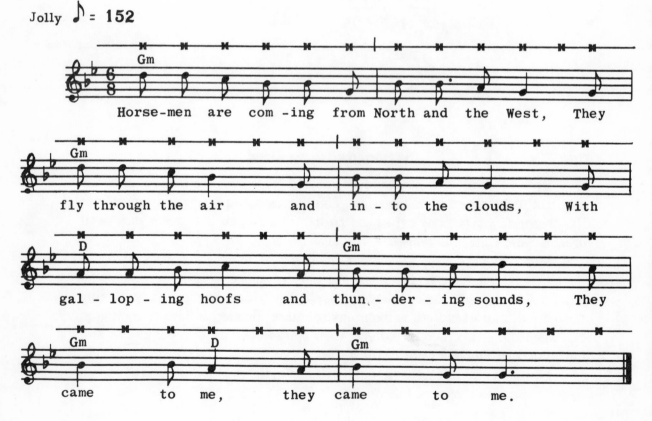

Jolly ♪ = 152

Horse-men are com -ing from North and the West, They fly through the air and in - to the clouds, With gal - lop - ing hoofs and thun - der - ing sounds, They came to me, they came to me.

Charging Thunder's Dream

Another storyteller was Charging Thunder, a very friendly man. The whole tribe liked him. Charging Thunder had a leading part in the Sun Dance at four different times. In this story he told us about his dream of the little wolves.

"When I was about twenty-two years of age, I dreamed that I came to a wolf den and found some little wolves all alone. They were crying and seemed to be saying, 'We are alone and helpless, but our parents will soon return.' I brought them some food and watched over them. Then they sang to me and I learned their song.

song of the young wolves

Gently and Slowly ♪.= **60**

Fa - ther is some - where, Moth - er is some - where, We are all a - lone, Some-thing is howl -ing, Some- thing is com -ing, We are all a - lone. They will be com - ing, They will be sing - ing, Ho - ly songs for home. We will greet them, When we see them, We won't be a - lone.

"Soon I saw the old father and mother wolves returning home. Old Father Wolf was pleased that I had taken care of his little ones, and as a reward for my good deed, showed me how to make a pipe that would protect me on the warpath. He then filled it with certain herbs and grasses, saying, 'When you smoke this pipe, it will give off a very strong smell. The enemy will be wondering where the smell comes from and will not notice you.' This pipe could outwit the craftiest warriors.

"I made such a pipe and when I carried it with me on the warpath, it brought success.

"The old wolf also taught me this song."

song of the old wolf

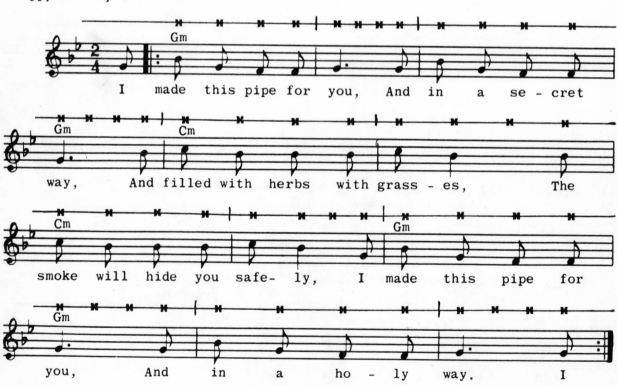

Happy and Gay ♪ = 112

I made this pipe for you, And in a se - cret way, And filled with herbs with grass - es, The smoke will hide you safe- ly, I made this pipe for you, And in a ho - ly way. I

The Moccasin Game

Four men played this game, two on each team. A blanket was spread on the ground and four moccasins placed in the center. A knife was tossed to decide which team would start the game.

Taking four little stones, one of which had a colored mark on it, a player placed a stone in each moccasin. As he was doing this, he would shake the stones in both hands, hum a song, and even make funny faces at the opposing team to make them laugh and look away. After the stones were distributed, a player from the other team would try to guess in which moccasin the colored stone was hidden.

When the time for guessing came, the humming would grow louder, and the player from the opposing team would stand up and point with a stick to the moccasin which he thought held the marked stone. The player making four correct guesses would win the game. The score was kept with small sticks. Sometimes the winner was given a blanket, a pipe, or some household article.

You can sing this song accompanied by drumbeats of your own choice. Place an *X* on the line above the melody where the beats sound best.

song of the moccasin game

Fast and Gay ♩ = 144

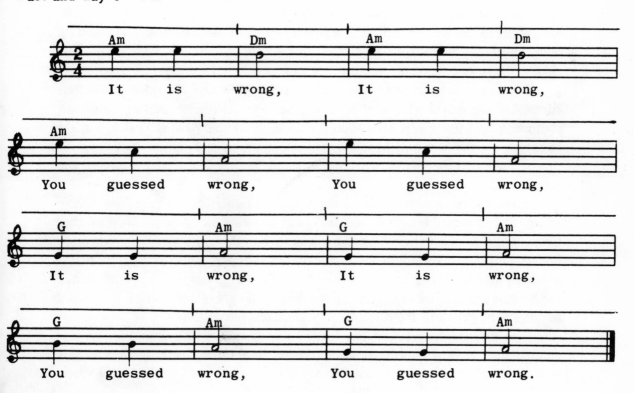

the pawnee indians

The Pawnee Indians were fine scouts, skillful hunters and brave warriors, and they called themselves "men of men." They fought against the Dakota and the Cheyenne, but were friendly to the white man. The name Pawnee comes from the Indian word *pariki,* which means "a horn." It was the custom of the Pawnee to shave the head, except for a narrow strip in the middle from the forehead to the back, and to stiffen the hair with grease and paint, curving it upward like a horn. They were good farmers and religious. The sun, moon and stars had special significance.

While living in Nebraska, they built villages and earthen lodges along the Platte River. The style of their homes gives a clue to their religious feelings. Entrances faced the rising sun; the round roof stood for the sky; and each post of a house represented a star. There was a place for sacred things at the west side of houses called *wiharu* ("a place for wonderful things"). Here was the garden of the Evening Star, where the corn ripened. A sacred bundle hung from one of the rafter poles, and sleeping space on either side of it was considered a great honor. The houses were forty feet wide and fifteen feet high. A family also owned a tepee which was used in summer and during the hunting season.

Legends

Tirawa was the great spiritual leader of the Pawnee, and was called Father. The heavenly bodies, the winds, the thunder, the lightning and the rain were his messengers. Next to Tirawa in power was Evening Star, who ruled in the west and was viewed as a woman. Then came Morning Star, a brave warrior who drove the other stars before him across the heavens. Morning Star ruled in the east, while in the west, Evening Star had a beautiful garden, a field of ripening corn, and many buffalo. From this garden sprang all the streams of life. The child of these two heavenly bodies, a son, was the first human being on earth.

Next in rank to Evening Star and Morning Star were the gods of the four corners of the world who supported the heavens in the northeast, southeast, southwest, and northwest (the sacred directions of the Pawnee). Below these in rank were the Sun and Moon, from whose union a daughter was born. In time she married the son of Morning Star and Evening Star, and produced the human race.

Each village was ruled by a chief and a council of leading men. Every village had a "sacred bundle" containing one or two ears of corn, called Mother Corn. The Pawnee believed that the sacred bundle came from the heavenly bodies. During the spring, at the first sound of thunder, a ceremony took place, at which time seed corn from the sacred bundle was given to the people. When the harvest came, another ceremony was held and ears of corn for all the sacred bundles were renewed from the freshly gathered harvest.

The first treaty between the United States and the Pawnee Indians was entered into at St. Louis in June, 1818. At that time a separate treaty was written for each village. A second treaty was set forth on October 9, 1833, at

which time the Pawnee gave back to the United States all land lying south of the Platte River. On April 10, 1876, a new Indian reservation was opened in Oklahoma, and the Pawnee were moved from Nebraska to this territory. By the terms of this treaty, a family (or single person over 21 years of age) could receive 160 acres of land. The United States government helped in building schools, roads and houses.

The Coyote and the Turkeys

In a village not far from a lake lived a coyote who had built a small earthen hut for storing his food and who kept busy with many little jobs. During the summer he went hunting in the forest and stored enough food for the winter months. When the snow and cold winds arrive, the forest is quiet and lonely. The squirrel, muskrat, chipmunk and beaver hide away. They have also stored food during the summer.

One day the coyote noticed that his food supply was low. He was also hungry, as coyotes always are, so he decided to go out and hunt.

He came to a hill and, looking down, saw a large flock of turkeys. "I am going to get one of them," he said. Crawling down the hill very slowly and quietly, he waited for his chance. But the turkeys spied him, huddled together and said, "Here comes a thief. He looks hungry. We must look out for him, for he is tricky." The coyote laid in wait quietly and watched. Then he said, "Grandchildren, let us play a game." The turkeys asked, "What kind of game?" The tricky coyote answered, "Well, let us not have a game, then. Let us have a dance." The turkeys now thought he was friendly, so they said, "All right, let us have a dance."

The coyote looked at the turkeys. He picked six of the biggest and plumpest, saying, "You must stand in the front," and then arranged two rows of turkeys in back of them. When the turkeys were all in place, he said, "I have a song. While you dance, you must close your eyes." He looked around and saw a turkey with its eyes open. "Close your eyes — you are looking at me!" he shouted. He continued singing and made sure that all had their eyes shut. Then he rushed at the turkeys in the front row and killed them. The rest flew away before he could get at them.

Then the coyote sat down for a big feast. But he brought some turkeys back to the village and stored them in his earthen hut. He even thought about giving some turkey meat to his friends.

With his song the coyote had deceived the turkeys. Not all were fooled, though. Some had flown away. They were smart. Or were they just lucky?

SONG OF THE COYOTE

the BEAR is pointing at the sun

Liesurely ♩ = **84**

Lis-ten to my song, Lis-ten to my song,

There stands a bear, There stands a bear,

Look- ing to the east, where the sun is ris -ing,

Yon -der stands a bear. Now the sun is ris -ing,

Giv - ing him the pow - er where the sun is ris - ing,

ris - ing, ris - ing.

The Bear is Pointing at the Sun

The sun, moon and stars had significance for the Pawnee Indians. Morning Star ruled in the east and Evening Star ruled in the west. All stars west of the Milky Way were thought of as womanly and those to the east as manly. The sun was near the Morning Star; the moon was near the Evening Star.

The Pawnee believed that the bear got his power from the sun, and that it was centered in his claws. How did this story come to the Pawnee tribe?

Long ago an old man named Lata'piu fell asleep in a meadow. When he awoke he saw a strange sight. A bear was pointing at the sunrise. He stood facing the sun and allowed the early rays of light to shine upon his paws, thus receiving the sun's power.

The old man made up a song about his vision, and whenever he saw the sunrise, he sang it. Ever since that time, the song has been a part of the Bear Dance ceremony.

I Am Like a Bear

At the Bear Dance ceremony, the tribe danced and sang about the wonderful power of the bear. They told stories about how he cured the sick and gave strength to the weak. The bear taught the tribe many songs and dances. A necklace made of bear claws provided wisdom and power.

A brave sang a song called "I am Like a Bear," which tells about a Pawnee who killed a Sioux and captured his horse. The song is in honor of the Pawnee's bravery. That is why the warrior sang:

"I am a brave man, acting like a bear.
Holding up my hands, for this rising sun."

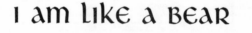

I am Like a Bear

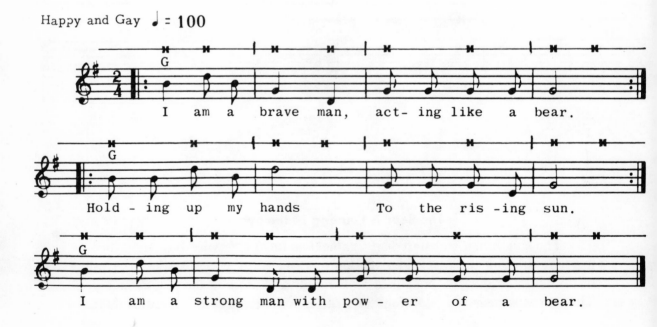

Happy and Gay ♩ = 100

I am a brave man, act-ing like a bear.

Hold-ing up my hands To the ris-ing sun.

I am a strong man with pow-er of a bear.

50

The Hand Game

When the Pawnee went traveling and stopped to rest, they would often play the hand game. At other times there would be a ceremony, including singing and dancing, before the game started. Men and women alike took part in the game, which sometimes lasted for hours.

A woman picked the leaders for each team, who in turn each chose four players. The object was for the opposing team to guess in which hand a player had hidden some small balls.

The player holding the balls did many tricks or deceptive movements in order to confuse the opposing team. First, he would shake the balls in both hands. Then he would place his hands above his head or behind his back. He would pass the balls to a teammate, or pretend to. While this was going on, everybody sang.

When the time came for guessing, the singing became louder and more frenzied. Then the player would hold out both hands and the opposing team would try to guess in which one the balls were hidden. The person who made five correct guesses in succession won the game.

hand game guessing song

Fast and Snappy ♪= 180

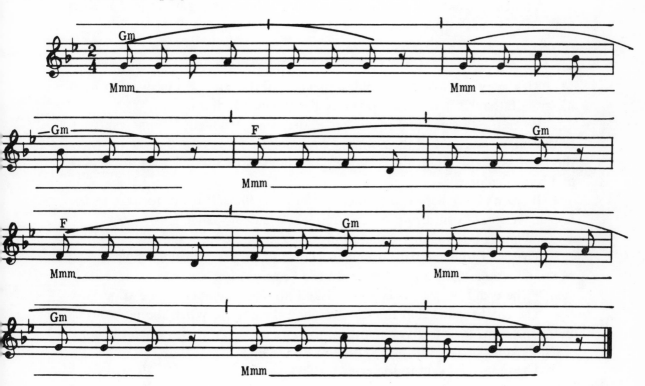

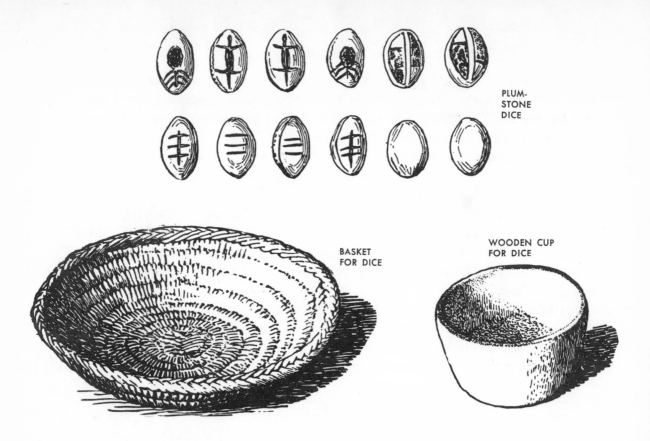

PLUM-
STONE
DICE

BASKET
FOR DICE

WOODEN CUP
FOR DICE

The score was kept with seven feathered sticks stuck in the ground.

Most game songs do not have words; they are chanted or hummed. If you want to hum this song or form a drumbeat, put in as many X's as you like on the line above the melody. This will then become your own, original rhythm.

You can repeat this song as many times as you like, getting louder each time, just as the Pawnee did.

The Pawnee and the Horse

This story was told by the oldest member of the tribe, who learned it from his grandfather. It is still told today by the Pawnee Indians.

When the Pawnee first saw a horse, they were frightened. Some ran back to the village and told of their strange find. Soon a large crowd came to where the horse was grazing in the meadow. The horse was spotted with gray, pink and brown colors.

It wasn't long before the chief of the tribe himself came to look at the horse. "Why are you afraid of this animal?" said the chief.

"What is he dragging behind him?" asked one of the Indians.

The chief told the tribe about the horse's tail. He told them how a flick of the tail could chase away flies and little bugs.

"Where did he get his colors?" asked another member of the tribe.

The chief replied that the sun provided the colors. When the horse feeds in the meadow, the sun gives him the grays and pinks. At night, when the horse rests, the dark heavens bring the browns and blacks.

Then the chief said to the crowd, "The horse is very useful. He will carry you and your packs. You can get on his back and he will take you from place to place so that you can hunt for game. Come, I will show you."

The chief walked up to the horse, holding two cornhusks. He offered one to the horse. At first, the horse neighed and stirred. The chief offered it again. This time the horse bent his head a little and ate the corn from the chief's hand. He patted the horse gently and got on his back. The chief rode the horse back to the village and the crowd followed, some mumbling and wondering.

Ever since that time, the Pawnee Indians have owned horses and found that they could do useful work.

you need not fear the horse

Moderate ♩ = **84**

Welcome Home, Pawnee Soldiers

On June 6 and 7, 1919, the Pawnee held a happy victory party. More than two hundred members of the tribe came to cheer, sing and dance. It was a welcome-home party for Pawnee soldiers who had fought in the United States Army during World War I.

Several of the Pawnee soldiers had been with the famous Rainbow Division. When there was a call for volunteers for dangerous action, four Pawnee had stepped forward and had been accepted. One of these men brought back a German Army helmet as a trophy. His mother carried it in the victory dance in the same manner as a scalp carried in former times. The helmet was fastened to a pole, at the top of which a captured knife had been tied like the point of a lance.

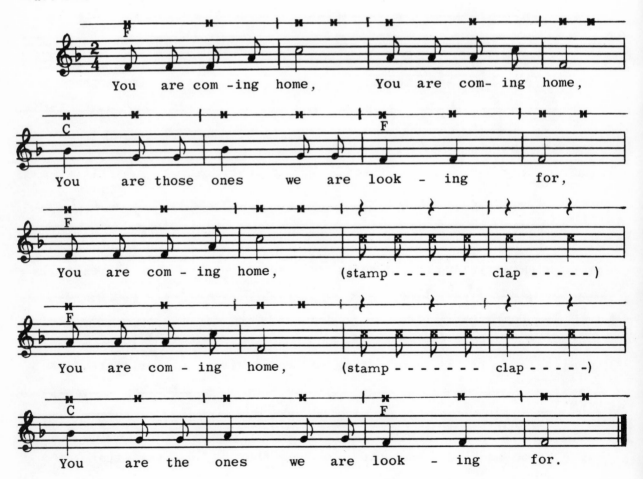

SONG FOR RETURNED PAWNEE SOLDIERS

Marchlike ♩ = 112

You are com-ing home, You are com-ing home,

You are those ones we are look-ing for,

You are com-ing home, (stamp - - - - - - clap - - - - -)

You are com-ing home, (stamp - - - - - - - clap - - - - -)

You are the ones we are look-ing for.

A Pawnee said, "While the boys were away, we prayed for their return. We did this at every public gathering. It looks as though our prayers have been answered."

This song was composed by John Luwak, a Pawnee Indian whose friends had read him newspaper reports of the war. John felt unhappy thinking of the boys across the ocean suffering so many hardships, so he prayed daily to Tirawa, father and leader of all the Pawnee, saying, "Help our boys over there, so they will all come back strong. Let me live to see them again."

One night, after such a prayer, he fell asleep. In his sleep someone told him that "it would not be long before he would see the Pawnee boys again." He dreamed, and in his dream he saw and heard thousands of people singing, dancing and waving flags; even the oldest people were dancing. A few days later he heard of the signing of the armistice, which meant the end of the war. The next night he dreamed again, and in his dream he saw a circle of Indians dancing and heard them sing this song.

Soon afterward, there was a gathering of the Pawnee. John Luwak arose, told of his dreams, and sang the song. The song was easily learned, and the people sang it at the party for the returning soldiers.

the papago indians

The name of this tribe comes from the Indian word *papah,* meaning "beans." Their original home was near the Gila River, south of Tucson, Arizona, and extended across the desert into Sonora, Mexico. They were a peaceful, farming people, raising maize, beans and cotton. Desert plants were also a source of their food. They ate the fruit of the giant cactus and from it made a wine offered at the rain ceremony. They traded in salt, which was taken from inland lagoons and sold in nearby towns and the cities of Tucson and Tubac.

Papago women were excellent basket-makers. At times these baskets were used as drums. They were also sold to visitors and stores in the city. Homes were round, with twigs, grass and leafy shrubs on the roof.

At the present time, the Papago Indians plant wheat and barley, raise cattle, make furniture and sell desert wood. Their village is near the San Xavier Mission which was first settled in 1692. The country around the village is desert land, but there are also rugged hills and deep gorges. The United States government runs four day schools in this area.

Legends

The Papago watched the stars. When they saw the Pleiades rise in the east in the evening and set in the west just before sunrise, they said the time had come for storytelling. The nights when these stars may be seen are the longest of the year. They told stories beginning with the creation of the world, and four nights were needed to tell all the old tribal stories. One of their stories was about Elder Brother, which is much like the Biblical story of Noah's Ark.

Musical Instruments

Four musical instruments were used by the Papago Indians.

1. Rattle: This was used with song to bring rain and for treating the sick.

2. Scraping Sticks: These were in pairs. One was slightly curved and notched. The other was smooth and used for rasping across the notched stick.

3. Basket Drum: A medium-sized basket in household use could also be used as a drum. It was turned upside down and struck with the hand. Three men could play this instrument at once by kneeling and striking it with their hands.

4. Flute: This was made from cane and had two small holes.

The Papago sang at ceremonies and when they told stories. They also participated in many game-songs such as the "Kicking-Ball Races" and the "Stick Game" song.

The Kicking-Ball Races

The Papago Indians enjoyed many sporting contests such as archery, shooting at a moving target, dart-throwing, ball games and racing. The most important was the kicking-ball races, requiring endurance and skill.

Two runners were in each race, and each one kicked a ball before him. After they reached the goal line, the runners turned around, kicking and running after the ball back to the starting point. The full distance was about a mile.

The balls were a little larger than a croquet ball, made of wood and covered with gum.

There was an old legend about a Papago Indian who wanted to be a good runner. He trained very hard for a long time. One morning he met a little animal on the road that said, "It seems as though you will never be a good runner, but I will give you a song and perhaps if you sing it, you will win the race."

The Indian learned the song, sang it, and won the race. When he had first met the animal, he was wearing the feather of the blue hawk in his headband. He believed, therefore, that the feather had helped him to learn the song, so he wore it for all of his races.

WE MUST RUN

Happy ♩ = 112

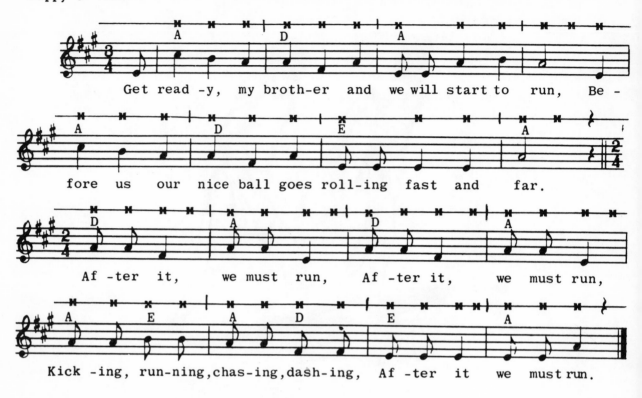

Get read-y, my broth-er and we will start to run, Be-fore us our nice ball goes roll-ing fast and far. Af-ter it, we must run, Af-ter it, we must run, Kick-ing, run-ning, chas-ing, dash-ing, Af-ter it we must run.

The Wine-Makers and the Watchers

The Papago began to prepare wine for the August rain ceremony during June, when the fruit of the cactus plant was gathered. The fruit grew at the top of the cactus, which was about twenty feet in height. After it was picked, it was boiled in water, strained to remove the seeds, and sealed in a barrel. The Indian name for the barrel was *olla*.

When the fruit was first put into water, one of the men would say, "I am mixing you up. Bring me a good wind and clouds of rain."

Four men watched the making of the wine. Two were on duty during the day and two during the night. They were also the "tasters." From time to time they would sip the wine and say, "Add some water," or "More syrup." These men rested while on the watch and had to sing four songs before rising to inspect the wine in the ollas. The four men and the four songs stood for the winds from the north, east, south and west.

The four "watchers" passed the wine to each other when it was finished, and many songs were sung. The leader would say to the man of the east, "Start a song." He would sing a song four times and all would join in at the fourth time. Then the singer of the east would say to the singer of the north, "I pass it on to you," and the singer of the north would sing a song four times. This went on to the singer of the south and to the singer of the west.

After the wine was passed around once and the songs were heard, everybody stood silent while a speech was made by the leader. He said, "My friends, you drink the wine that I have prepared for you. If any one of you have the power to bring the rain, let him ask the lightning doctor, whose name is Mocking Bird, to send the best kind of wind, and after that, the best kind of clouds. Ask him to send the white clouds, and after that, the black clouds. In them is the thunder and the lightning which we welcome because we know they bring good to us. We hear the sound of thunder in the mountains around us. Let us all join in our feeling to have the rain. Let us all be glad to see the water running in the little washes to moisten the fields where we plant our seed. The plants that come up will be green and beautiful in the fields, and when they have finished growing, we will get the food for which we are now hoping."

song of the watchers

With Expression ♩ = 94

The ea - gle is fly- ing a- round and a -round, He's
mak - ing a sha - dow___ on the ground, The
blue hawk is fly - ing in a straight line, He's
mak - ing a sha - dow___ thin and fine, I
run a -round the sha - dow___ hop -ing for the wind.

The Rain Ceremony

In the early part of August the Papago held a festival, at which time the medicine men prayed for rain and good crops. An important part of the ceremony was the drinking of wine (*tiswin*) made from the fruit of the cactus plant.

This song is from an old legend about a little boy who had the power to make rain. He taught the mothers of the tribe, directing them to take the fruit of the cactus plant, mash it, and boil it for an hour. Then they were to strain it, put it in a barrel and seal it. The little boy began to sing the song about the rain. He gave the people many songs and told them to sing these songs to bring the rain.

I BRING THE RAIN

With Much Feeling ♩ = 94

Here I sit and with my pow - er,

I bring the South Wind t'ward me,

Af - ter the wind, I bring the clouds,

Af - ter the clouds I bring the rain

That makes the flow - ers grow, ___

That makes the home ground beau - ti - ful.

The Stick Game

The stick game (called *ginskut*) was a favorite with this tribe. It was played every afternoon.

Four gaming sticks were used, each with a special decoration. Stick No. 1 had four lines which indicated the four days' fasting of a brave warrior on his return from a victory. Stick No. 2 represented bird's claws. Stick No. 3 pictured the rays of the sun. Stick No. 4 showed the lines and colors of paint on the face of a warrior.

The ground was marked with a square, each corner of which had a group of ten dots. One corner had a loop of dots called the "house."

A player took the four sticks in his hands and rested them on a stone so that the ends were exactly together. Then he struck them with a stone, causing the sticks to fly into the air. When they fell, the sticks nearest to the corners were counted. Each stick was worth a certain number of points. No. 1 was worth six points and No. 4 was worth only two points. A good player would try to cause the stick having the highest value fall near the corners of the square. The score was kept by moving a stone alongside the dots. The player who reached the "house" with the highest number of points won the game.

To sing this song with a drum-beat accompaniment, write in your own rhythms on the line above the melody with *X* marks.

I will toss up the sticks

Marchlike and Even ♩ = 104

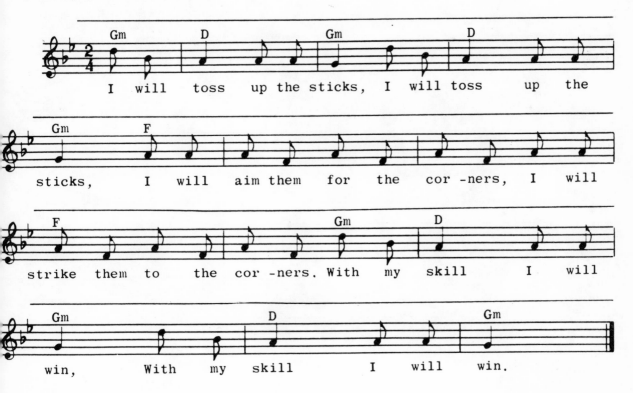

I will toss up the sticks, I will toss up the sticks, I will aim them for the cor-ners, I will strike them to the cor-ners. With my skill I will win, With my skill I will win.